NELSON
MANDELA

BY EMANUEL CASTRO   ILLUSTRATED BY IGNACIO SEGESSO

Raintree is an imprint of Capstone Global Library Limited,
a company incorporated in England and Wales having its
registered office at 264 Banbury Road, Oxford, OX2 7DY
– Registered company number: 6695582

www.raintree.co.uk
myorders@raintree.co.uk

ISBN 978 1 4747 5144 5 (paperback)
21 20 19 18 17
10 9 8 7 6 5 4 3 2 1

By Emanuel Castro
Illustrated by Ignacio Segesso

British Library Cataloguing in Publication Data
A full catalogue record for this book is available from the
British Library.

Translated into the English language by Trusted
Translations

Printed and bound in China.

CONTENTS

Little Nelson was impressed. He didn't know there could be such a rich home just a day's walk from his village.

5

Jongintaba Dalindyebo was the ruler of all the Transkei tribes. The white South African government allowed them to fix their own disagreements.

But Jongintaba was not alone. He was supported by the amaphakati, or wise elders, who advised him.

We have a problem. Can you explain it, Bomokhu?

We all know there is a drought. Our livestock are dying of thirst. Except Chief Ngonume's, since a creek runs through his land.

Let's divert the creek so that it will run through as many villages as possible.

If we did that, some of your animals would survive, but there is not enough water, and none of it would reach my land. All my animals would die.

Is that fair, Regent Jongintaba?

6

They stood in silence. The Great Chief Jongintaba had not spoken during the entire session.

Until now.

We have reached a decision. Let all the villages herd their cattle to the part of the creek nearest to them.

That way, they'll all be able to drink the water and survive.

Everyone cheered. No one would have thought of making such a decision. Befitting of his rank, the great chief had found the perfect solution.

You see, my son. A leader is like a shepherd who stays behind the flock.

He allows the most fit to travel in front, followed by the rest, who never realize that they are, at all times, being guided from behind.

7

Jongintaba was a great chief. He knew how to repay those who had walked long distances to participate in the hearing.

But in another room, the amaphakati held a meeting in accordance with their rank.

Nelson didn't dare go in, but he wanted to listen to the wise ones.

I'll die soon. That doesn't make me sad. We all die, sooner or later.

I'm just sad about not seeing the Africa I saw and heard in my youth.

Our heroes, like Sekuhune, king of the Bapedi, won't return.

Or the warriors of King Ngangelizwe, who fought the white invader with their bravery and spears. Klam! Klam! Klam!

Klam! Klam! Klam!

8

CHAPTER 2
RADICAL WORDS

Nelson Mandela was 20 years old. The Great Chief Jongintaba had paid for his university studies.

He was sent to Fort Hare, the largest university south of the African equator.

Hey, Nelson! Did you hear? The Germans invaded Poland! This is war!

The end of the year and the graduation ceremony had arrived. But that year, it was something special. Jan Smuts, the former prime minister, had been invited to speak to the graduating class – an honour for Fort Hare.

And South Africa must support the United Kingdom in this fight against Nazism.

Esteemed students, the world has gone to war.

13

15

That day, Mandela began to understand that a black man did not have to put up with the small abuses to which he was subjected day after day.

CHAPTER 3
A BETTER COUNTRY

1942. The war continued, far away, though it touched North Africa.

Nelson, could you draft this document for me? It's from the Walton Case, File 3563/7.

That did not stop Mandela from completing his law studies through a correspondence course at the University of South Africa. He got his first job at the Witkin, Sidelsky and Eidelman law firm.

Of course, sir. Why didn't you call me to go get it?

You mean, why did I bring it to you personally?

Yes, sir, that's what I meant.

Well, I hadn't really thought about it. Are people of colour supposed to be the white man's errand boys?

Yes, sir, supposedly.

19

25

CHAPTER 4

JOURNEY TO THE ROOTS

1948. The National Party, chaired by Reverend Malan, won the elections – elections that were only for whites. Apartheid, the policy of racial segregation and discrimination, deepened.

Comrades of the African National Congress...

Not only are we required to show "pass books" on the street for any reason, but we are not even allowed to move through white neighbourhoods.

The time has come to act, to demonstrate nonviolently against these awful acts.

Nelson Mandela has worked so hard within the Congress that he becomes a member of the Executive Committee.

Dr Moroka, a longtime member of this committee, does not agree. But we are not just Moroka, we are 100,00 members of the HNC.

That is why I'm proposing a nonviolent action for tomorrow. I need volunteers who know they will be arrested for going into white neighbourhoods.

The next day, the demonstration began.

More than 200 people were arrested.

Mayibuye Afrika*!

It was to be expected, but I will volunteer for the next day.

Nelson Mandela!

You're under arrest!

30

* Bring back Africa.

31

Days later, the trial came to an end.

I find the defendants guilty and sentence them to nine months in jail and forced labour.

But given the nonviolent nature of the crime, the sentence is suspended for two years.

Many things occurred leading up to the year 1961. A divorce from Evelyn, another four-year trial in which Mandela was found innocent, and a second marriage, to Winnie Madikizela.

The apartheid policy got stronger, and the banning of the ANC forced Mandela to hide out on a farm.

I have thought about it a lot, and I need your opinion. I believe that the nonviolent struggle has run its course.

The ANC needs to have an armed wing to create government instability. Do you agree?

YES!

All right. We'll call it Umkhonto we Sizwe*. We'll use this farm as its headquarters, and I'll go underground to organize it.

* Spear of the Nation.

33

At this point, the existence and struggle of the African National Congress and the Umkhonto we Sizwe had got the whole world's attention.

Nelson! A letter has arrived for you from Addis Ababa!

I can't believe it. A colonel is inviting me to Ethiopia to offer us help.

Nelson, it is an honour to have you in Ethiopia.

And it is an even greater honour for me that you've decided to support us.

How could we not? Except for those five years of Italian occupation, we were never colonized.

35

Having fulfilled his mission in Ethiopia, Mandela knew he was one step closer to fulfilling a dream of his youth...

... a visit to Egypt.

He was like a young boy. He took notes on everything.

That's what he was looking for.

Any proof that he could use to fight the false statements that Africans lacked a civilized past.

The Egyptians were creating works of art while Westerners still lived in caves.

38

44

47

50

51

CHAPTER 6

AFRIKA MAYIBUYE

By 1988, Nelson Mandela's situation had changed drastically. He had been moved to a house that had windows, a swimming pool and was surrounded by trees, in the back of another prison.

But the outside had also changed. The armed struggle was growing. And not just the one led by the ANC, but ones led by other, more radical groups as well.

Maybe President Botha believed that Mandela could do something to bring peace.

Nelson Mandela was called to a secret meeting led by Justice Minister Coetsee.

We are interested in starting negotiations with you, Dr Mandela. But you must first help end the armed struggle.

I know you're the head of intelligence, Dr Barnard. Are you here to spy on me? I'll have you know that I have nothing to hide.

As head of intelligence, I must see to it that these negotiations come to pass. I consider myself your friend, Mandela. Believe me.

55

57

59

But things were getting complicated. An armed group, opposed to the ANC, had become strong during Nelson Mandela's years in prison.

"Inkatha" has murdered 50 people in cold blood, Mr Mandela. We must stop this rising violence.

I know what I must do. Organize a rally at the stadium in Katlehong.

Katlehong? But it's the very home of Inkatha! You'll be in grave danger!

I have been all my life. Why should I be afraid now?

No one opposed it. But President de Klerk feared that Mandela would suffer an attack, which would deepen the violence.

De Klerk set up an impressive security operation, but that would be of little use if anyone attempted anything against Mandela.

61

In truth, freedom had brought Mandela more problems than solutions.

Endless meetings with political opponents, trips and interviews with world leaders caused his relationship with Winnie to crack. But he was not alone. He had his children. And something more...

Mr Mandela? Are you awake? You have an important call.

Put it through on this line, will you?

I'm sorry? Did you say Nobel Peace Prize?

In fact, he had won the Nobel Peace Prize, jointly with de Klerk.

I take this opportunity to confirm that there has never been a prize so deserved as the one that has also been awarded to Dr Frederik de Klerk.

He had the courage to admit that a terrible injustice had been committed against our country and our people through the use of the apartheid system.

He had the foresight to understand and accept that all the people of South Africa must together determine what they want to make of their future.

Meanwhile, the general elections drew closer...

We're not as sure as you, Mr Mandela.

General Viljoen is a hard nut to crack.

Hard or soft, we must reach an agreement with him before the April elections.

But he threatened to start a civil war!

That's exactly why. I want to establish trust, and show that I'm not going to accuse him of treason.

His charisma is still strong within the army, and he could certainly carry out his threat.

Dr Mandela, General Viljoen is here.

General, I'm happy you accepted my invitation.

But before our groups meet to go over the details, I'd like to talk to you for a minute, alone.

Please, have a seat.

Would you like some tea, general?

Oh, yes. Thank you.

Milk?

Why not?

Sugar?

Good grief! Will you at least let me stir it?

Mandela knew at once that the tough General Viljoen was learning to trust his eternal enemy.

Mandela's intention of not showing bitterness was as successful as he had hoped.

67

And so, a Nobel Peace Prize winner named his friend, Archbishop Desmond Tutu, another Nobel Peace Prize winner, the chairman of the Truth and Reconciliation Commission.

A ruling was made that all children in schools would receive a piece of bread with butter to fight the hunger that had continued in the country for centuries.

The economy experienced such a boost that it resulted in a previously nonexistent class, the great black middle class.

In addition to the Nobel Prize, Mandela received countless international awards and honourary doctorates from many other universities, as well as a bronze statue in his honour in the city of London.

For centuries, Nelson Mandela will be remembered as a leader who fought for justice and freedom.

NELSON MANDELA

TIMELINE
1918-2013

1918	1930s	1940s	1950s
Mandela is born on 18 July 1918, in the village of Mvezo, with the name Rolihlahla Mandela. He is the son of the chief adviser to the Thembu king. In 1925, he attends school, where his teacher renames him Nelson.	Mandela's father dies, and he is handed over to the care of the Thembu regent, Jongintaba Dalindyebo. In 1934, he attends the Clarkebury Institute. In 1937, Wesleyan College. In 1939, he enrolls at University College, Fort Hare.	Mandela is expelled for joining a student protest. In 1941, he moves to Johannesburg, escaping an arranged marriage. He meets Walter Sisulu and, in 1942, works at the law firm of Witkin, Sidelsky and Eidelman. In 1943, he completes his studies at the University of South Africa. In 1944, he co-founds the Youth League of the African National Congress (ANC) and gets married for the first time. He begins his law studies, which he will leave and return to over the years.	First convictions for Mandela's political activity. In 1952, he is sentenced to nine months of forced labour for a civil disobedience campaign against unjust laws. In 1953, he designs a plan for the ANC's future secret actions. He is arrested again in 1955 and found not guilty in 1956, after the trial.

1960s	1980s	1990s	2000s
Banning of the ANC, which goes underground. In 1961, Mandela founds the armed wing of the ANC, Umkhonto we Sizwe. In 1962, he travels to Morocco and Ethiopia for military training. He is arrested upon returning to South Africa and is sentenced to five years in prison. In 1963, the Rivonia Trial is held. Mandela is sentenced to life imprisonment in 1964 and sent to Robben Island.	In 1982, Mandela is moved to Pollsmoor Prison. In 1985, he rejects President Botha's first release offer. In 1988, after several health issues and being diagnosed with tuberculosis, he is sent to Victor Verster Prison, where he spends 14 months in a house. In 1989, he earns his law degree from the University of South Africa.	End of the ban on the ANC. Mandela is released from prison and elected president of the ANC. In 1993, he receives the Nobel Peace Prize, shared with President de Klerk. In 1994, he votes for the first time in his life, along with the rest of the black population of South Africa. He is elected president of the Republic of South Africa. In 1999, he ends his term and retires from politics.	In 2003, Mandela starts the Mandela Rhodes Foundation. He retires from public life in 2004. In 2008, he asks future generations to continue fighting for social justice. He dies on 5 December 2013 in Johannesburg.

WHO WAS NELSON MANDELA?

Nelson Mandela was one of the most important political figures of the 20th century. He was an example to the world when it comes to searching for peace.

Mandela was born in 1918, and, from an early age, looked to the leaders of his tribe, the Thembu, as his mentors. He began his own political career at age 24 when he joined the African National Congress (ANC). This organization carried out peaceful campaigns against the apartheid system, which subjected South Africa's black population to discrimination and segregation. In 1943, Mandela founded the ANC's Youth League, carrying out civil disobedience campaigns protesting government decisions against blacks. During these years, he was arrested and sentenced to forced labor.

In the 1960s, the ANC's political activity was banned. Nelson Mandela went on to form an armed wing of the party to resist government repression. As part of his military training, he secretly traveled to Ethiopia, the only African country that had never been subjected to European colonialism. Upon returning, he was arrested and sentenced to life in prison during the famous Rivonia Trial. He was sent to Robben Island, where he stayed for more than 20 years.

In 1990, Mandela was released after the ban on the ANC was lifted. In 1993, he was awarded the Nobel Peace Prize, and, in 1994, he was elected the first black president of the Republic of South Africa.

During his presidency, Mandela forgave those who had abused his people for so many years. He did so for the sake of the peaceful rebuilding of his nation. His words during the Rivonia Trial in 1964 were a perfect example of his life's purpose: "I have fought against white domination, and I have fought against black domination. I have cherished the ideal of a democratic and free society in which all persons live together in harmony and with equal opportunities. It is an ideal to live for and to achieve. But if needs be, it is an ideal for which I am prepared to die."

MANDELA AND FILM

Nelson Mandela has often been depicted in films, TV series, and TV movies throughout the years. His life was, without a doubt, worth remembering on film. One of the first movies to portray his life was a TV film, made in 1987, when Mandela was still in jail. Danny Glover played Mandela in that version.

The year 1997 saw the release of the movie *Mandela and de Klerk*, which looks at Mandela's life from his time in Robben Island until his release. Mandela was played by American actor Sidney Poitier, who, in 1963, was the first African American to win an Oscar for best actor. De Klerk was played by Michael Caine, who, in 1975, had already starred opposite Poitier in a film about apartheid, *The Wilby Conspiracy*.

The most recent biopic about Mandela is *Mandela: Long Walk to Freedom*. The movie is based on Nelson Mandela's autobiography, which shares the same title. Mandela's character was played by British actor Idris Elba, but the first choice was Morgan Freeman.

Coincidentally, Morgan Freeman played Mandela in *Invictus*, a thrilling film directed by Clint Eastwood, which is about President Mandela's support of the South African rugby team during the 1994 World Cup. In this sport, which was practiced only by whites, Mandela saw a chance to unite the entire South African people and heal the wounds of so many years of discrimination and violence.

Nelson Mandela was not only a character in movies, but he also participated as an actor in the film *Malcolm X*. In it he makes a brief appearance as a schoolteacher in South Africa.

SOUTH AFRICA AND APARTHEID

In Afrikaans, the Dutch variant language used in South Africa, "apartheid" means "separation". It was a system of racial discrimination in South Africa from 1948 until 1990.

At that time, only 21 per cent of the South African population was white. But it had imposed its control over the black and mixed-race majority since the previous century.

In 1948, after Daniel François Malan was elected prime minister, a mandatory racial registry was established to separate the population. Marriages between blacks and whites were officially banned in 1949. The main goal of the ban was to separate the races by giving whites more legal power than anyone else, but the separation also applied to where people lived. By 1950, only whites could live in certain urban areas, which forced large numbers of blacks to move to rural areas.

At the same time, cities had "whites-only" and "blacks-only" sections, the latter being of lower quality. Segregation reached its highest levels when, in 1959, blacks were assigned to small segregated territories called the Bantustans. They were also denied South African citizenship.

In addition, as of 1954, the black population was fully banned from taking part in political life. This included a ban on holding positions at any level of government, as well as a ban on voting, except for some exclusively black institutions.

Public transportation was also segregated. In the 1950s, Nelson Mandela organized a civil disobedience campaign within the African National Congress against all these limitations, actions that led to his first arrests.

Until the 1960s, protests took the form of passive resistance of the government. People organized marches protesting segregation, and these were generally met with violence by the government. This changed with the banning of the black majority parties, the African National Congress and the African Congress Party. From then on, passive resistance turned into armed struggle. Nelson Mandela became the leader and organizer of his party's armed wing. But in 1963, with a state of national emergency having been declared, he and many other political leaders were arrested and sentenced to life in prison.

During the 1970s, violence peaked during the events known as the "Soweto Massacre". In 1974, the government ruled that the Afrikaans language was mandatory in all schools, including those of the black population. Two years later, the schools of Soweto, an exclusively black district, rebelled by conducting marches and demonstrations. On 16 June 1976, one of those marches ended in a brutal police action, which left 566 children dead and began a wave of violence throughout South Africa.

At the international level, the South African government became increasingly isolated. The country suffered strong economic sanctions, or trade limitations, from other nations and was not allowed to take part in the 1964 Olympic Games.

The isolation had a negative effect on South Africa's economy, resulting in a growing crisis. Finally, even the white minority that controlled the country realized the need to end apartheid. Between 1989 and 1994, President Frederik de Klerk, working with Nelson Mandela, took the necessary measures to bring to an end more than 50 years of segregation and injustices. In 1994, Nelson Mandela was elected as the first black president during the first free elections in the history of South Africa.

GLOSSARY

activist person who works for social or political change

apartheid former policy of racial segregation and discrimination in South Africa

BBC British Broadcasting Corporation; a British public service broadcaster that produces radio and TV shows

Boer group of Dutch origin that settled in the territory of South Africa and Namibia in the 17th century. They were the dominant white minority in the territory until the end of apartheid in 1992.

boycott refuse to take part in something as a way of making a protest

charisma special magnetic charm or appeal

colonialism practice of gaining full or partial political control over another country and using it for economic gain

communist person who believes in a system in which goods and property are owned by the government and shared in common

correspondence course course of study in which students and teachers communicate by mail

demonstrate join together with others to protest something

discrimination treating people unfairly because of their race, country of birth or gender

domination control over something through the use of strength and power

inferiority complex feeling like one has less value than someone else

inflation increase in prices

negotiation talking to reach an agreement

occupation taking over and controlling another country with an army

oppress treat someone in a cruel, unjust and hard way

propaganda information spread to try to influence the thinking of people; often not completely true or fair

radical extreme compared to what most people think or do

reconciliation restoring friendly relations between groups of people

regime government in power

resignation giving up a job, position or office

revolutionary wanting to bring about major changes to the government of a country

segregation separating people because of their skin colour

siege surrounding of a city to cut off supplies and then wait for those inside to surrender

treason act of betraying one's country

underground secret and done without government approval

DISCUSSION QUESTIONS

1.   Who do you think had the greatest influence on Nelson Mandela's political life? Explain your answer.

2.   Lazer Sidelsky, Mandela's first boss at the law firm, warns him that politics will only bring him problems. Do you agree with him? Do you think he was right? Discuss your thoughts with your classmates.

3.   What do think the differences are between passive resistance and active resistance? What do you think was the best way of opposing apartheid at that time? Illustrate your answer with an example from Mandela's life.

WRITING PROMPTS

1.   Imagine that you are a news reporter for your country in South Africa on the day of Mandela's freedom. Write an article about what happened from your country's perspective.

2.   Put yourself in the shoes of one of Robben Island's political prisoners. Write a brief message (that could fit inside a matchbox) to the common prisoners to organize a protest about one of your complaints.

3.   Imagine that, as an adult, Mandela writes a letter to himself as a child. What do you think he would say to himself?